COUNTRY

Vol. 49, No. 4

Publisher, Patricia A. Pingry
Editor, D. Fran Morley
Art Director, Patrick McRae
Editorial Assistant, Tim Hamling
Contributing Editors, Lansing Christman,
Deana Deck, Russ Flint, Pamela Kennedy,
Nancy J. Skarmeas, John Slobodnik

ISBN 0-8249-1100-8

IDEALS—Vol. 49, No. 4 June MCMXCII IDEALS (ISSN 0019-137X) is published eight times a year: February, March, May, June, August, September, November, December by IDEALS PUBLISHING CORPORATION, P.O. Box 148000, Nashville, Tenn. 37214. Second-class postage paid at Nashville, Tennessee, and additional mailing offices. Copyright © MCMXCII by IDEALS PUBLISHING CORPORATION. POSTMASTER: Send address changes to Ideals, Post Office Box 148000, Nashville, Tenn. 37214-8000. All rights reserved. Title IDEALS registered U.S. Patent Office.

SINGLE ISSUE—$4.95
ONE-YEAR SUBSCRIPTION—eight consecutive issues as published—$19.95
TWO-YEAR SUBSCRIPTION—sixteen consecutive issues as published—$35.95
Outside U.S.A., add $6.00 per subscription year for postage and handling.

ACKNOWLEDGMENTS

KNEE DEEP IN JUNE and TO AN OLD FARM HOUSE by Edna Jaques from *BESIDE STILL WATERS*, copyright © 1952, published in Canada by Thomas Allen & Son Limited. TEACH THEM THE FLAG by Edgar A. Guest from *THE PASSING THRONG*, copyright © 1923 by the Reilly & Lee Co. Used by permission of the author's estate. Our Sincere Thanks to the following authors whom we were unable to contact: Inga Gilson Caldwell for OLD BARNS; Anne Campbell for FOLLOWING THE PLOW; Bertha Hudelson for SUMMER SEARCHING; Rose Marie Overman for FOR BOYS IN SUMMERTIME; Bess Truitt for COUNTRY MAIDS

Four-color separations by Rayson Films, Inc., Waukesha, Wisconsin

Printing by The Banta Company, Menasha, Wisconsin
Printed on Weyerhauser Lynx

The paper used in this publication meets the minimum requirements of American National Standard for Information Sciences—Permanence of Paper for Printed Library Materials, ANSI Z39.48-1984.

Unsolicited manuscripts will not be returned without a self-addressed stamped envelope.

Inside Front Cover
George Hinke

Cover Photo
Superstock, Inc.

Inside Back Cover
Francis Chase

Following the Plow

Anne Campbell

There's a pleasure of my childhood
I know my boys will miss.
On cloudless days in summer
There is no joy like this;
Barefooted and bare-headed,
With sweat upon my brow,
I've counted every furrow
While following the plow.

The earth was fascinating,
Fresh-turned and rich and black.
I used to look for angleworms
As we went on and back.
The cool ground felt so grateful,
I feel it even now.
There never was such pleasure
As following the plow.

They were mighty handsome horses,
The sorrel and the bay.
We stopped them at the furrow's end
To pass the time of day.
My grandpa puffed a corncob,
And I remember how
His trail of smoke blew past me
While following the plow.

Near the fence rail lay a treasure,
Some bottled lemonade,
And many cooling sips we took
There in the peaceful shade.
But oh, what joy at twilight
When Grandpa said, "I 'low
You'd better ride that off-horse home
From following the plow."

Old Barns

Inga Gilson Caldwell

Old barns retain a mystic quality.
Within high raftered beams, the scent still clings
Of fragrant clover mixed with timothy;
Between the wide spaced boards, a wind harp sings
While sunlight forms pipe organ patterns on
The spacious floor where dust motes dance at will.

Within the choir loft, in union,
Birds sing their choral music, versatile
In repertoire as any symphony.
Above a stable barn once, long ago,
A star of prophecy bent down; and so
Old barns retain a mystic quality.

Photo Opposite
HORSE FARM
Connecticut
Larry Lefever
Grant Heilman Photography

Photo Overleaf
ROLLING FARMLANDS
Near Baraboo, Wisconsin
Dietrich Photography

To an Old Farm House

Edna Jaques

I like old houses that are weather-stained,
  Whose doorstep sags beneath the weight of years,
Old walls that echo back with softened tone,
  The laughter that we knew, the sound of tears.

Old treasured quilts with tiny stitches made,
Bits of gay dresses that our mothers had,
Old pictures in an album gray and dim,
A little blue-eyed boy, that once was Dad.

Old, roomy kitchens steeped in fragrant food,
  The shining stove, its welcome gracious cheer,
Old cellars made of stone, with crib and bin,
  Storing with pride the harvest of the year.

Old parlors hushed and clean, stiff chairs arrayed,
  In stately rows beside the shining wall,
A feather wreath, a gaudy painted fan,
  The stilted splendor of a Chinese doll.

Old homes that breathe of peace and quiet hours,
  That we in happy dreams may see again
And taste the perfume of her glowing flowers,
  Dim as forget-me-nots in summer rain.

COUNTRYMAN'S GOD

Arthur Thatcher

The peace of summer rests upon the fields . . .
It is apparent with the day's first light

And lingers on through all the sunny hours,
Until replaced by gentleness of night.

The peace of summer brings a perfect calm . . .
The mighty trees in woodlands seems to sleep

With branches waiting for a stirring breeze,
Until some zephyrs o'er the landscape creep.

The peace of summer has a restful touch . . .
No matter if some fear or worry chides,

For nature speaks a language of her own
To tell mankind of One who still abides.

CALUMET FARMS
Lexington, Kentucky
C. Peter Gridley
FPG, International

Photo Overleaf
SWIMMING HOLE
Original Artwork by John Sloane

Country Vegetables

Earle J. Grant

Tawny golden peaches,
Red tomatoes, too;
Green and yellow peppers
Drenched in sparkling dew.

Plump watermelons,
Green-gold cantaloupes;
Rosy, tart rhubarb
Festooning clay slopes.

Rare stained-window skies,
Green corn, mile on mile. . .
All of these make up
Summer, country style.

Photo Opposite
GARDEN SHED
Larry Lefever
Grant Heilman Photography

Cantaloupe Swirl Cheesecake

1 medium cantaloupe
1¼ cup sugar (divided)
4 tablespoons cornstarch (divided)
1 tablespoon lemon juice
3 eight-ounce packages cream cheese
¼ teaspoon salt
½ teaspoon almond extract
5 eggs

Cut the cantaloupe in half and remove the seeds. Cut each half into wedges and cut the rind from the fruit. Cut the fruit into 1-inch pieces and put into the container of an electric blender or food processor. Add ¼ cup sugar, 2 tablespoons cornstarch, lemon juice, and a dash of salt and blend until smooth. (There should be about 2 cups of puree.) In a small saucepan, bring the pureed mixture to a low boil; reduce heat and simmer, stirring, for about five minutes or until thickened; let cool.

In a large bowl, beat softened cream cheese with electric mixer until light and fluffy. Beat in 1 cup sugar, 2 tablespoons cornstarch, ¼ teaspoon salt, and almond extract. Add eggs one at a time, beating well after each addition. Pour the batter into a buttered 9-inch springform pan. Spoon the cantaloupe puree evenly over the batter. Draw the tip of a knife through the mixture in swirls. Bake in a preheated 325° oven for 50 minutes.

Turn off oven and let cake remain in oven with door closed for an additional 30 minutes. Remove cheesecake to wire rack and cool to room temperature. Cover loosely with plastic wrap and chill for at least eight hours before serving. To serve, remove the sides of the springform pan, place cheesecake in center of large serving dish, and garnish with fresh melon balls.

Photo Courtesy Texas Fresh Promotional Board
Cary Whitenton, Photographer

Deana Deck

Melons

There's nothing more luxurious on a summer's morn than to step out into the garden and pick a juicy breakfast of fresh cantaloupe or honeydew melon. While there are only a few areas of the country where oranges or grapefruits can be picked fresh for breakfast, home-grown melons can be enjoyed almost anywhere, and they don't even require an in-ground garden.

Melons should be grown in rich, well-drained soil. A garden patch works fine, but a large tub or even a five-gallon flower pot will work. Many varieties have been bred especially for container gardening: Musketeer and Bush Star cantaloupes and New Hampshire Midget and Bush Sugar Baby watermelons will produce nicely in a container when provided with a trellis for their vines. All melons can be started indoors from seed, but the correct time for transplanting outdoors varies according to geographic location.

Northern gardeners have a saying: "Plant melons in May, throw them away. Plant in June, they come just as soon." Of course, the further south, the earlier melons can be started. Night temperatures should be in the sixties for best results. Melons love heat and produce the best fruit in hot weather. However, melons also require plenty of water, so hot, dry summers are not conducive to melon growing.

All melons require lots of water and good drainage. For in-ground or container grown melons, mix sand, peat moss, and other organic matter into the soil to make it rich and loose. Containers need to be large enough to allow for adequate drainage. Plastic mulch can be used to keep the plants from drying out; it is also a good way to control weeds.

Once several small melons have developed on the plant, pinch off the fuzzy ends of the vines so that the plant will divert its energy from vine growth to fruit development. In mid-season, remove the smallest melons to provide the larger ones with more nutrients. As the melons grow, it's important to support the weight of the fruit. This can be done with cheesecloth slings or with old pantyhose and a trellis. With cheesecloth, cut a twenty-inch long length of fabric; tie one end to the trellis. Slip the cloth hammock-style under the melon and tie the other end to the trellis. A support made of pantyhose will not only hold the melon off the ground but will help protect it from insects. Cut one leg from the pantyhose; cut off the foot section. Cut the remaining piece in half; knot the end of one length, and slip the melon inside. Knot the other end and tie it securely to the trellis. Raised off the ground, well-supported melons will develop better and be less vulnerable to disease and pests, although melons are subject to the same woes that beset cucumbers and squash.

Aphids, squash vine borers, squash bugs, and cucumber beetles will do the most damage to melons. To help control pests, cover the vines with spun polyester row cover material (available at garden shops or through most garden catalogs) and weigh down the edges with bricks or large rocks. Insects can also be controlled with bug sprays, but only use sprays formulated for fruits and vegetables.

Check for ripeness seventy-five or eighty days after planting short-season melons. Cantaloupes will have the recognizable sweet, earthy fragrance when they are ready for harvest. Don't bother thumping watermelons to test for ripeness; it is not a sure sign. Instead, watch the small tendril located at the point where the melon stem adheres to the vine. When this tendril turns brown and dries up, the watermelon is ready for harvest.

Harvesting the first melon will be a special occasion. On that summer day, walk out to the garden with pride. Pick the melon, slice it open and enjoy the luxurious, fresh taste of a home-grown melon for breakfast or dessert.

Deana Deck lives in Nashville, Tennessee, where her garden column is a regular feature in The Tennessean.

Garden Man

It never failed that every year
Summer would again appear;
And with it came the Garden Man
Of whom I was his biggest fan.

Each morning when I would awake
He was there for the garden's sake.
But little did he know or see,
That he was also there for me.

Mom would have to leave all day
Which left me home to work and play.
Peace I had within my heart
Since he was there right from the start.

Our garden grew, our grass was green,
Yet there was more to this, I've seen;
For one thing that for sure I knew
This man, my dad, to me was true.

Jill Elizabeth Zeitlow
New Haven, Indiana

Garden Memories

I'm thankful for the memory
Of a garden, long ago,
Where I saw my father stand
At dusk, leaning on his hoe.

His face was as peaceful
As the soft twilight glow,
While his eyes surveyed
Each neatly worked row.

For the soil was his easel,
The brush was his hoe,
And the picture he completed
Was the lovely vegetable row.

Now I wish, upon the canvas
I could paint a masterpiece
Of my father in the garden
Where his day's work whispered peace.

Belle Banister Broadbent
Clarksville, Tennessee

20

Reflections

Father's Day

Over the years
As we grow old,
We remember our father
So brave and bold.

In the garden,
Leaning on the plow,
He would listen to me;
I see him now.

He would give advice
And understand;
He was always there
To lend a hand.

God made fathers
Strong and firm,
For he knew our lives
Would have great concerns.

So he gave us fathers
To teach us to pray,
And guide our lives,
And show us the way.

So on his day
Let's take the time
To say "Thanks, dad.
I'm glad you're mine."

Mary Frances Bogle
DeKalb, Illinois

Bless a Farm Dad

Linda C. Robinson

I wish that you could know a man
Who views a greening, plush farmland
And sense the feeling that he knows
Of tasseling corn in long, straight rows.

He sees that same corn reappear
In countless hills, from year to year;
Yet, never do I fail to trace
A hint of awe upon his face.

His skin is tinged a red earth tone
Where fifty summer suns have shone,
And underneath his straw hat brim
Are hazel eyes and stalwart chin.

Sinewy hands and arms so strong
From sending bales of hay headlong
Have succumbed to a gentler task
And cradled up a newborn calf.

It never fails . . . he always knows
Just where to find the first wild rose
And gathers several fragrant blooms
To grace a small farmhouse's rooms.

I hear his prattle at early dawn
Calling his "little cattle" on.
And later, as the dusk draws nigh
He croons an Irish lullaby.

Another day, another night,
He heads toward shining farmhouse lights
And softly breathes a thankful prayer
For the loving family waiting there.

God, bless this farm dad all his days
That we, his children, might convey
The welling sense of pride we've known
From such a fine example shown.

FATHER & DAUGHTER
FPG International

My Dad & I

Phyllis C. Michael

My dad and I—we think alike,
  He knows just what I mean
Before I even say a word
  He reads, well, in between.

My dad and I—we like to fish
  Or build a model plane,

FATHER & SON
FPG International

Or fix a broken chair or two
   Or just a windowpane.

My dad and I—we know the score
   Of every single game;
Sometimes he's really busy, too
   But he takes me just the same.

My dad and I—we go swimming too,
   Each year and sometimes twice.
My dad and I—we do everything;
   My dad—he's really nice.

FOR BOYS IN SUMMER

Rose Marie Oberman

In summertime, my Grandpa's farm
Held nearly every well-known charm
For boys who loved to wander free
With cheerful birds for company.

Almost as soon as we'd arrive,
Some new adventure we'd contrive—
Along the creek; out on the lea;
Or in the tallest apple tree.

Grandmother cautioned lovingly,
"Be careful, now!" I'm sure that she
Realized her well-meant advice
Afforded just a bit of spice.

With miles of room for ball, croquet,
And every kind of boyish play,
We'd pause just long enough to eat
Some of Grandma's home-baked treats.

And even though her table fare
Was quite the best served anywhere,
'Twas still a standing escapade—
The berry patch and garden raid!

Ripe berries, still warm from the sun,
Would please the taste of anyone;
But oh, what taste could ever match
The pleasures of the melon patch!

Along a pleasant woodland trail;
Up rocky slope; through grassy vale;
We'd wander as the hours sped by—
Bright hours that seemed to sanctify.

The country twilight—peaceful, still—
Made every heart with reverence fill.
My Grandpa's farm in summertime
Was surely close to the sublime.

Little Robin Redbreast

Little Robin Redbreast
  sat upon a tree;
Up went Pussycat,
  and down went he.
Down came Pussycat,
  and away Robin ran;
Said little Robin Redbreast,
  "Catch me if you can."

Little Robin Redbreast
  jumped upon a wall;
Pussycat jumped after him,
  and almost got a fall.
Little Robin chirped and sang,
  and what did Pussy say?
Pussycat said naught but "Mew,"
  and Robin flew away.

Knee Deep in June

Edna Jaques

Knee deep in June—in grass and purple vetch
　With songs from every hedge and clump of scrub,
A flock of blackbirds swooping by the door,
　The iridescent colors of a grub.

A broody hen stealing her nest away,
　Hiding her little clutch of precious eggs,
A yellow kitten dozing in the sun,
　A new colt trying out his slender legs.

The strong brave roots that grow from rotten stumps,
　Sending up tiny shoots to make a tree,
A grey squirrel running on a cedar fence,
　The busy journeys of a honey bee.

A cowbird calling someone in the dusk,
　A farmer's wife humming a little tune,
A happy child singing her doll to sleep,
　And all the world drowsing knee deep in June.

Each June

Garnett Ann Schultz

Each June we quickly find again
So much from Junes before,
The birds on wing that gayly sing
Outside our open door.

Each June is like a thousand past,
And yet, it seems so new.
In happy bliss, we share all this;
So much we love to do.

A June day vibrates with the song
Of birds the whole long day;
Not just at morn or evening hours,
They ever bless our way.

A treasured sweetness, yet more dear;
A world so much in tune.
Serenity and quiet peace:
'Tis these we find each June.

31

Summer Searching

Bertha R. Hudelson

Summer days hold jewels
That sparkle with rare light
Of rainbow flowers in daytime,
And polished stars at night.

Watch a morning glory,
In frail summer dress
Meet with pastel sparkle
A sun and wind caress.

Watch a velvet pansy,
Sweet-faced, smiling, shy,
Greet with jewel-like colors
Every passerby.

Wisteria and daisies,
Their colors bright but brief,
Are part of earth's jewel-beauty
With charm beyond belief.

Summer days hold jewels
That meet the questing eye.
Come! Let us go searching
For others, you and I.

WISTERIA VINES
Al Riccio
New England Stock Photo

THE FIREFLIES' DANCE

Jane Carroll Route

The fireflies were dancing one night,
A summer night in June.
They danced to the trees' sweet melody,
The wind's soft, gentle tune.

They do-si-doed around the tree,
Had a square dance in the grass.
Along the walk the held a waltz,
And curtsied as they passed.

They smoothly danced the minuet,
Each shining like a star;
They chose their partners in the air,
But never wandered far.

They floated past the maple tree,
Their dances filled with mirth.
They danced the night without a sound
Like stars that fell to earth.

A Day in June

James Russell Lowell

What is so rare as a day in June?
  Then, if ever, come perfect days;
Then Heaven tries earth if it be in tune,
  And over it softly her warm ear lays;
Whether we look, or whether we listen,
  We hear life murmur, or see it glisten;
Every clod feels a stir of might,
  An instinct within it that reaches and towers,
And, groping blindly above it for light,
  Climbs to a soul in grass and flowers;
The flush of life may well be seen
  Thrilling back over hills and valleys;

The cowslip startles in meadows green,
  The buttercup catches the sun in its chalice,
And there's never a leaf nor a blade too mean
  To be some happy creature's palace;
The little bird sits at his door in the sun,
  Atilt like a blossom among the leaves,
And lets his illumined being o'er run
  With the deluge of summer it receives;
His mate feels the eggs beneath her wings,
  And the heart in her dumb breast flutters and sings;
He sings to the wide world and she to her nest—
  In the nice ear of Nature, which song is the best?

In the Good Old Summertime

Helen Colwell Oakley

In June, Mom allowed us to go barefoot around the farm. It was fun on the velvety grass, but my feet never could take the pebbles or the sharp blades of grass. My playmates could run over the stones and prickly fields like the wind, but my feet never got tough enough so that I could race barefoot with the wind, through the fields of grain on a beautiful day in summer.

In the good old days, we did not have swimming pools, but we had the old swimming hole. The water was cool and refreshing. We splashed and played with the inner tube in the water. Cows and horses frequently came to the water's edge to drink, and this was sort of frightening as we thought they might be wild, but they never were. They just took a long drink,

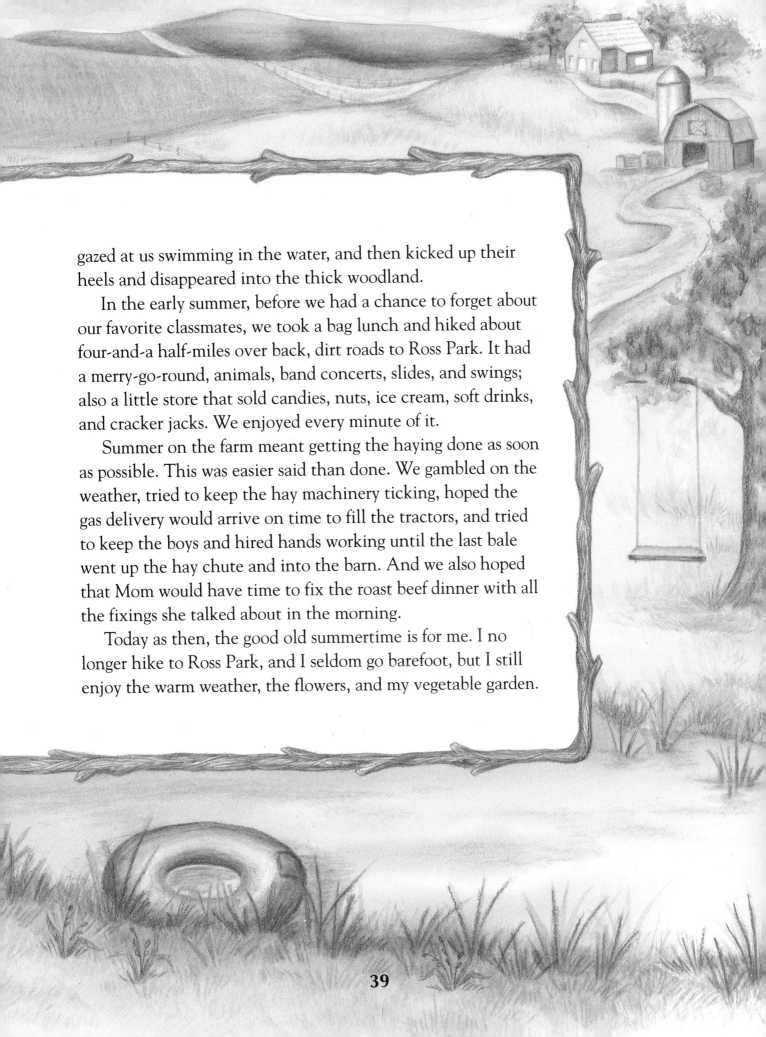

gazed at us swimming in the water, and then kicked up their heels and disappeared into the thick woodland.

In the early summer, before we had a chance to forget about our favorite classmates, we took a bag lunch and hiked about four-and-a half-miles over back, dirt roads to Ross Park. It had a merry-go-round, animals, band concerts, slides, and swings; also a little store that sold candies, nuts, ice cream, soft drinks, and cracker jacks. We enjoyed every minute of it.

Summer on the farm meant getting the haying done as soon as possible. This was easier said than done. We gambled on the weather, tried to keep the hay machinery ticking, hoped the gas delivery would arrive on time to fill the tractors, and tried to keep the boys and hired hands working until the last bale went up the hay chute and into the barn. And we also hoped that Mom would have time to fix the roast beef dinner with all the fixings she talked about in the morning.

Today as then, the good old summertime is for me. I no longer hike to Ross Park, and I seldom go barefoot, but I still enjoy the warm weather, the flowers, and my vegetable garden.

A Song of Summer

Margaret E. Sangster

The ships glide in at the harbor's mouth,
    And the ships sail out to sea,
And the wind that sweeps from the sunny South,
    It's as sweet as sweet can be.
There's a world of toil and a world of pains,
    There's a world of trouble and care,
But oh, in a world where our Father reigns,
    There is gladness everywhere!

The harvest waves in the breezy morn,
    And the men go forth to reap;
The fullness comes to the tasselled corn,
    Whether we wake or sleep.
And far on the hills by feet untrod,
    There are blossoms that scent the air,
For oh, in this world of our Father, God,
    There is beauty everywhere!

The babe lies soft on the mother's breast,
    And the tide of joy flows in.
He giveth, He taketh, He knoweth best,
    The Lord to Whose home we win.
And oh, when the soul is with trials tossed,
    There is help in the lifted prayer!
For never a soul that He loves is lost,
    And our Father is everywhere.

The ships sail over the harbor bar
    Away and away to sea.
The ships sail in with the evening star
    To the port where no tempests be.
The harvests wave on the summer hills,
    And the bands go forth to reap,
And all is right, as our Father wills,
    Whether we wake or sleep.

40

Photo Opposite
EAST CHOP LIGHTHOUSE
Martha's Vineyard, Massachusetts
Johnson's Photography

Nancy J. Skarmeas

John James Audubon

On October 12, 1820, John James Audubon boarded a flatboat on the Ohio River headed south from Cincinnati toward New Orleans. He carried with him the tools of his future—a gun, a portfolio of drawings of wild birds, black chalk, and a set of watercolors. It was the beginning of what he would later call "The Great Idea," a project that would span eighteen years and would make the name Audubon synonymous with the appreciation and protection of America's wild birds.

Born to a French merchant in 1785 on the West Indian island of San Domingo, Audubon spent most of his childhood in Nantes, France.

42

With his father often absent, John took advantage of an indulgent stepmother and neglected his formal studies in favor of the more fascinating outdoor world around his country home. At eighteen, Audubon left France for Mill Grove, a two-hundred acre farm outside of Philadelphia, purchased by his father some years earlier. Though he spent less than two years there, it was at Mill Grove that Audubon's interest in birds became a consuming passion. He hunted but was not satisfied by the hunt or the kill; he turned to drawing as a way to preserve the beauty of the living bird.

Audubon's peaceful and solitary existence at Mill Grove was interrupted by Lucy Blackwell, the daughter of his British neighbor. The two fell in love, were married, and moved to Henderson, Kentucky, where Audubon planned to operate a store. Audubon, however, found his desire to wander the woods in search of new species of birds in conflict with the need to make money and support his wife. For more than a decade, he struggled with this conflict. In 1820 he finally gave up the idea of being a store owner and decided to make his passion for birds his business. "The Great Idea" was a plan for a series of life-size watercolors of wild American birds in their natural habitats, to be engraved, printed, and sold by subscription.

For the next eighteen years, Audubon pursued his Great Idea with all the fervor he had lacked in his earlier venture. He supported himself and his family by painting portraits for five dollars apiece, but he was always on the lookout for new species of birds for his portfolio. After three years of work in the Southeast, Audubon traveled north to Philadelphia to find an engraver and publisher to begin production of his series which he called *The Birds of America*.

Success was not awaiting Audubon in Philadelphia, however; he made more enemies than friends in the city. In May of 1826, he set sail for Liverpool, England, sure that he would find an audience for his work. Within ten days of his arrival, he had an exhibition of paintings. The man who had seemed self-aggrandizing in Philadelphia was received warmly in England as a rugged American frontiersman with a genius for painting. Before the year ended, he had found an engraver and publisher.

For the next twelve years, Audubon traveled from the Florida Keys to the coast of Labrador, and as far west as Arkansas, to collect 489 distinct species of birds. The birds were rendered life-size with accurate natural backgrounds, many of which were painted by other artists. In addition to *The Birds of America*, Audubon published, with the assistance of Scottish author William MacGillvary, a companion volume, *Ornithological Biography*, which combined descriptions of the birds, their habitats, and their behavior with tales of Audubon's own adventures in the wilds.

Audubon worked tirelessly on his project. In addition to his travels, he solicited subscriptions in England and America and supervised the engravers. He was separated from his family more often than not, and several times near bankruptcy as he sunk his own funds into production.

In the end, however, Audubon's "Great Idea" of 1820 earned its title. Audubon solicited one hundred and sixty-one subscribers, each of whom paid one thousand dollars for the series. *The Birds of America*, *Ornithological Biography*, and subsequent mini-editions of his paintings supported his family quite comfortably.

The Great Idea, however, was more than a successful financial venture. Audubon single-handedly created a natural history of American birdlife which opened the eyes of America and Great Britain to the precious resources of the natural world. Audubon's dramatic, life-size paintings created a new awareness of the beauty and variety of America's wild birds; this awareness became a prerequisite for future efforts at conservation and protection. Audubon himself may be no model for the modern conservationist. He was, after all, a hunter who in his lifetime killed thousands of wild birds in service of his art. In that respect, he was a man of his time, but the achievement of his eighteen years of devotion to the wild birds that he loved is a model for anyone concerned with protecting the environment. For Audubon, the birds always came first.

Mill Grove

Photo Courtesy Mill Grove
Audubon Wildlife Sanctuary
Audubon, Pennsylvania

The history of Mill Grove seems intrinsically connected to the accomplishments of its most famous tenant, John James Audubon, the nineteenth century artist and naturalist who lived less than three years on the vast estate in southeastern Pennsylvania. Today's visitor will find a museum and wildlife sanctuary devoted to Audubon's work, but a thorough investigation of Mill Grove reveals the estate's rich and varied history.

In 1762, James Morgan, a Pennsylvania businessman, built a spacious mansion amid a grove of trees overlooking Perkiomen Creek in Montgomery County, Pennsylvania. The picturesque estate included an operable grist mill which combined with the wooded location to provide the descriptive title Mill Grove, a name which has endured as long as the structure itself. Morgan employed his brother, Thomas, as caretaker of the home. Thomas kept Mill Grove as a hostelry, providing room and board to weary travelers.

The first two decades of Mill Grove's existence were perhaps its most trying. The estate endured several owners; and during the Revolutionary War, both British and American soldiers looted the estate for food, horses, and other provisions. In 1789, the estate was owned by Augustin Prevost, but he soon sold Mill Grove to Frenchman Jean Audubon, the father of the famous naturalist.

Jean Audubon found Mill Grove very attractive, but not for the natural beauty his son would find so appealing. The ongoing French Revolution jeopardized Jean Audubon's economic resources; consequently, he sought a safe investment in America for his wealth. Mill Grove provided the perfect solution. The estate's natural resources included an abundant lead mine among the fields and woodlands. After purchasing Mill Grove, Jean Audubon hired a tenant farmer to manage its upkeep; he returned to France with his resources safely invested and never again returned to America.

In 1804, John James Audubon moved to America and into his father's estate. The fields, valleys, streams, and groves completely captivated the eighteen year old. He freely roamed the estate's acres studying and drawing the wildlife he discovered. Audubon's interest in ornithology blossomed during his few years at Mill Grove. By 1808 when he left Mill Grove, Audubon had established a sound artistic foundation for the detailed paintings that would eventually secure his future.

Mill Grove again endured several owners until Samuel Wetherill purchased the estate in 1813. Like Jean Audubon, Wetherill was attracted to the estate for its lead mines. He owned a major paint manufacturing company in Philadelphia, but his business was suffering because the War of 1812 had significantly limited the importation of lead to America. Mill Grove's lead mines salvaged Wetherill's business.

In 1830, copper ore was also discovered on the property. The copper and lead mines combined to boost the area's population and economy. Nearby towns prospered from the influx of miners hoping to strike it rich. By the mid-nineteenth century, however, the deposits dwindled, and the mines were finally abandoned. Mill Grove, however, remained in possession of the Wetherill family, who lived peacefully and elegantly on the estate's expanses.

In the late 1800s, William H. Wetherill, a descendent of Samuel, began promoting Mill Grove as the first American home of John James Audubon. The great naturalist's success and popularity brought local as well as national interest to the estate. Finally, in 1951, the Montgomery County Commissioners purchased Mill Grove.

Today, Mill Grove serves as a museum and wildlife sanctuary preserving the major works of its most famous tenant, John James Audubon. The museum houses complete editions of all Audubon's written and artistic works, including a first edition of *The Birds of America*, the original copperplate engravings that established his fame as a natural artist. The attic of the mansion has been restored to resemble the studio where Audubon first drafted his sketches. Murals decorating the main floors' walls recreate Audubon's first experiences at Mill Grove and depict the multitude of plant and animal life on the grounds.

As impressive as the Mill Grove mansion is, the grounds are even more stunning. Most of the original acreage has been preserved in its natural state. Walking trails allow visitors to explore the same forests and fields as Audubon. In the forty years of County ownership, over 175 species of birds and over 400 species of plants have been identified. Visitors who take the time to explore the grounds can truly experience the same abundant gifts of nature as Audubon once did. In 1989, Mill Grove was designated a National Historic Landmark to ensure that its natural abundance flourishes for future generations.

Mill Grove inspired John James Audubon's passion to record and preserve the natural world around him. It is only fitting that Audubon's talent and fame helped preserve the very estate that inspired his career.

THROUGH MY WINDOW

Pamela Kennedy

Cross-Country

When we received word of my husband's new assignment on the East Coast, I dragged out the dog-eared atlas. There I could see the entire USA, from sea to shining sea. The spidery webs of freeways and secondary roads tantalized me as they spanned mountains, valleys, prairies, and deserts. The idea of a family journey crept into my mind, a cross-country adventure, a contemporary quest. We could spend quality time together in the van as we rolled along the highways and byways, getting better acquainted with one another and the land of our birth. Humming "America the Beautiful," I began to plan. We would stop at scenic vistas, quaint out-of-the-way villages, eat ethnic foods in the different regions through which we passed.

While I contemplated being on the road with Charles Kuralt, my mate, with whom I would actually be traveling, was firing off inquiries to the automobile club requesting the shortest and most direct route from California to Washington, D.C. That should have been my first clue—the trip might not be precisely what I had in mind!

"But there are no scenic vistas on the interstate!" I cried, "No out-of-the-way villages!"

"That's the point," my practical spouse replied with a satisfied grin. "I figure if we're up by five each morning, we can hit the road while the kids sleep and get at least one hundred miles under our belts before breakfast. Think what that will do to our daily mileage average!"

"Think what it will do to our quality time!" I wailed.

In the end I lobbied for and won two days at the Grand Canyon and a drive through the "nevertobeforgotten" Petrified Forest. He got one hundred miles before breakfast.

We pulled into our hotel on the edge of the Grand Canyon at dusk, and I immediately signed us up for the horseback ride to an "authentic western barbecue" the following evening. It would be wonderful, something the kids could always remember.

Around midnight, the thunder began, and the room was illuminated with blue-white flashes of lightning. It rained all night, and in the gray, dripping morning, we dashed across the parking lot to the restaurant for breakfast.

"I bet it will stop by noon," I offered. No one looked convinced.

We spent most of the day traipsing from lookout to lookout along the canyon's rim, straining over the edge to glimpse the scenic vistas through the rain-clogged valley below. "I think I see something!" shouted one of the children. It was not what I had envisioned.

By four that afternoon, the wooded trails were rippling brooks, and it was clear the horseback ride and barbecue under the stars were out of the question. We settled on the "Wonders of the Grand Canyon" at the theater with a wraparound screen that puts the viewer in a rubber raft careening down the rapids of the Colorado River.

"How about those vistas?" whispered my husband. I whacked him with my program.

The next morning there were rainbows on the horizon as we headed for the Petrified Forest. It would be a good day, I was sure. After taking several wrong turns and discovering a multitude of out-of-the-way places, we rolled into the forest. My daughter was immediately disappointed, having expected an entire forest—trees, ferns, bushes and bunnies—all turned into stone as if in some life-sized fairy tale. The boys, however, were appropriately impressed with fossil remains and stony tree trunks and spent their allowances on chunks of rock with unpronounceable names. I tried to impress the children with the immensity of time, the great forces of nature, but the only forces of nature interesting them were hunger and thirst. After a quick stop at the snack bar, my husband informed me we could still make one-hundred and fifty miles before nightfall if we hit the road now.

Able to discern a losing battle, I herded the children into the van and we headed east. In the next days, we passed through flat prairies and rolling woodlands, magnificent cities and small towns. We stopped at waysides and roadside eateries, striking up conversations with truckers and travelers and visitors from foreign countries.

We spent hours telling jokes and riddles and singing ridiculous songs, dozing now and then as the humming of the tires lulled us to sleep.

The last few miles on the Capitol Beltway were filled with anticipation as we each eagerly waited for our first glimpse of Washington, D.C.

"Look," my son shouted, "the Washington Monument!"

We all gazed in silence at the slim, straight tower piercing the summer sky. Within minutes other famous landmarks came into view—the Jefferson Memorial, Arlington Cemetery, then the Capitol Building gleaming in the bright, afternoon sun.

"It's just like in the history books!" observed my astonished daughter. "Boy, this certainly is some country!"

My husband took my hand in his and smiled. "How about that for a vista, Mrs. Kuralt?"

I shook my head with resignation and chuckled. "Yes," I agreed, "and to think, we made it in record time."

Pamela Kennedy is a freelance writer of short stories, articles, essays, and children's books. Married to a naval officer and mother of three children, she has made her home on both U.S. coasts and in Hawaii and currently resides in Washington, D.C. She draws her material from her own experiences and memories, adding bits of imagination to create a story or mood.

A Song for Summer

S. Omar Barker

Summer is a singing bird,
　　Downy-fluffed and clean,
Against the sky a winging bird
　　Feathered all in green.

Summer is a willow tree
　　Waltzing with the flow
Of wind across a meadow lea
　　Where wild flowers grow.

Summer is a gypsy tune
　　Echoed in the heart;
Never can it come too soon
　　Nor too late depart!

MOUNT HOOD
Cascade Range, Oregon
Jeff Gnass Photography

AMERICA THE BEAUTIFUL

Katherine Bates

O beautiful for spacious skies,
  For amber waves of grain,
For purple mountain majesties
  Above the fruited plain!
    America! America!
  God shed his grace on thee,
And crown thy good with brotherhood
  From sea to shining sea!

O beautiful for pilgrim feet,
  Whose stern, impassioned stress
A thoroughfare for freedom beat
  Across the wilderness!

America! America!
God mend thine every flaw,
Confirm thy soul in self-control,
Thy liberty in law.

O beautiful for heroes proved
In liberating strife,
Who more than self their country loved,
And mercy more than life!
America! America!
May God thy gold refine
Till all success be nobleness
And every gain divine!

O beautiful for patriot dream,
That sees beyond the years,
Thine alabaster cities gleam
Undimmed by human tears!
America! America!
God shed His grace on thee,
And crown thy good with brotherhood
From sea to shining sea!

July

Margaret Rorke

July is a soldier saluting his flag;
So proud of his country he's given to brag
'Bout all of her virtues, her wisdom, her lore:
A swain to the lady he's come to adore.

July can relax in his own summer sun,
Completely ignoring what ought to be done.
He relishes picnics and ball games and such.
Vacations and gard'ning he likes very much.

July, as a person, is youth at high time,
Developing fully but not at his prime.
He's vibrant, warm-hearted, and eager to try;
Life's harvest is still but a gleam in his eye.

A SLICE OF LIFE

— Edgar A. Guest —

Teach the Children of the Flag

Teach the children of the Flag,
    Let them know the joy it holds
    In its sun-kissed rippling folds;
Don't let patriotism lag:
    Train them so that they will love
    Every star and stripe above.

As you teach their lips to pray,
    Teach them always to be true
    To the red, the white, and blue;
Praise the Flag from day to day,
    Tell the children at your knee
    All the joys of liberty.

John Slobodnik

Let them know and understand
How the Flag was born and why;
Tell how brave men went to die
Gladly for their native land;
Whisper to them that they must
Make the Flag their sacred trust.

Love of country ever starts
In the home and at your knee;
There the Flag shall come to be
Shrined in patriotic hearts;
They shall gladly serve their land
When they know and understand.

Edgar A. Guest began his illustrious career in 1895 at the age of fourteen when his work first appeared in the Detroit Free Press. *His column was syndicated in over 300 newspapers, and he became known as "The Poet of the People."*

The Flag Goes By

Henry Holcomb Bennett

Hats off!
Along the street there comes
A blare of bugles, a ruffle of drums,
A flash of color beneath the sky:
Hats off!
The flag is passing by!

Blue and crimson and white it shines,
Over the steel-tipped, ordered lines.
Hats off!
The colors before us fly;
But more than the flag is passing by.

Sea-fights and land-fights were great,
Fought to make and to save the State:
Weary marches and sinking ships;
Cheers of victory on dying lips;

Days of plenty and years of peace;
March of a strong land's swift increase;
Equal justice, right and law,
Stately honor and reverent awe;

Sign of a nation, great and strong
To ward her people from foreign wrong:
Pride and glory and honor, —all
Live in the colors to stand or fall.

Hats off!
Along the street there comes
A blare of bugles, a ruffle of drums;
And loyal hearts are beating high:
Hats off!
The flag is passing by.

56

Photo Opposite
UNITED STATES MARINE BAND
SSgt. Joe Steele, Photographer

Women's Army Auxiliary Corps

Josephine Ripley

There have been more important dates in the history of the United States. But May 27, 1942, will surely go down on the record. It was the day that women joined up with the Army—the first Women's Army Auxiliary Corps in American annals. From long before dawn until well after dim out, 440 recruiting stations throughout the nation were struggling to keep pace with the avalanche of patriotic response unloosed by the call for 540 women candidates for officers' training.

When enlistments closed on June 4, the War Department had not only its officer material, but the names of hundreds as well who had indicated their willingness to consider this as enrollment in the ranks, if they were not among those selected for special training.

Most amazing of all to those who watched was the mood of these women. Here were no excitement seekers looking for a thrill. These are no glamour girls in search of the spotlight. They were in earnest, all of them, motivated by a common, sober impulse—to help win the war.

They represented a cross section of American society, without a section missing. . . . There were pretty girls, plain ones; rich and poor. "I have five brothers in the service already," said one. And another: "My husband was at Pearl Harbor." Still another: "If a man can give up his life for his country, certainly a woman can give up her time."

Some were disappointed. They will not be assigned to pilot a bomber, to fire ack-ack guns, or to engage in any type of combat service. Those who were not citizens and those not yet 21 were crestfallen, too. But the faces of women between 45 and 50 brightened. A last-minute ruling of the War Department extended the age limit to include them in this enlistment in the officer corps.

Two top qualifications, both in recruiting of officers now and in the general recruiting for the ranks, which begins on Sept. 1, will be the quality of leadership and a good moral character. A pleasing personality is also essential, as well as a neat appearance, a tactful manner, and general adaptability.

On July 15, 450 women, selected by the War Department out of the 540 which have been drawn from Army Corps areas throughout the country, will report for an eight-week training course at Fort Des Moines, Iowa.

Those who complete that course most successfully will be appointed officers, their rank to be determined by their performance in training. Others will be appointed noncommissioned grades, and be eligible for appointment as officers later, as the Women's Army Corps expands.

It won't be any picnic joining the Army. It will be eyes front when they go by shop windows from now on. There won't be a closet full of frocks to choose from in the morning. There won't be time off whenever they happen to want it. There'll be a 30-day furlough whenever Uncle Sam gives it to them.

While in the Officer's Training School, the women will receive $50 a month. After the course is completed, a First Officer will be entitled to draw $166.67 a month, a Second Officer $131.25, and a Third Officer $125.

In addition, living quarters are supplied and a subsistence allowance of 60 cents a day. In lieu of living quarters, there would be an allowance of $40 a month. Noncommissioned officers will be paid according to grade. First Leader, $72 a month; Leader, $60 a month; Junior Leader, $54 a month. An auxiliary (buck private) will receive $21 a month, for the first four months, and $30 a month thereafter.

Girls may be asked to report as hostesses, accountants, telegraph operators, clerks, machine operators, cooks, stewardesses, dietitians, librarians, or in other capacities where they may release men for combat service.

Their term of service is for one year, but may be extended by the Secretary of War for the duration, and for not more than six months thereafter.

Yes, they're in the Army now, and they'll be good soldiers, these American women. They gave assurance of that on May 27th, and the days following. They have proved it in the past, at Plymouth Rock, in the covered wagons rolling West, and they're ready to write another chapter in history today.

from *The Christian Science Monitor*, June 20, 1942

I Hear America Singing

Walt Whitman

I hear America singing, the varied carols I hear,
Those of mechanics, each one singing his as it
  should be blithe and strong,
The carpenter singing his as he measures
  his plank or beam,
The mason singing his as he makes ready for work,
  or leaves off work,
The boatman singing what belongs to him
  in his boat, the deckhand singing
  on the steaming boat deck,
The shoemaker singing as he sits on his bench,
The hatter singing as he stands,
The wood-cutter's song, the ploughboy's on his way
  in the morning, or at noon intermission,
  or at sundown.

The delicious singing of the mother,
  or of the young wife at work,
  or of the girl sewing or washing,
Each singing what belongs to him or her,
  and to no one else,
The day what belongs to the day—
  at night the party of young fellows, robust, friendly,
Singing with open mouths
  their strong, melodious songs.

BITS & PIECES

As long as our government is administered for the good of the people, and is regulated by their will; as long as it secures to us the rights of persons and of property, liberty of conscience and of the press, it will be worth defending.

President Andrew Jackson

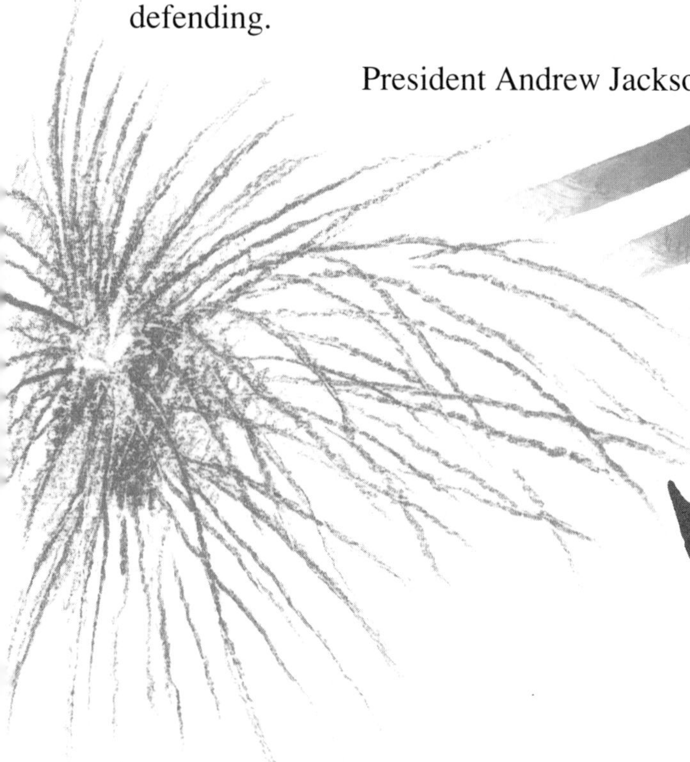

Liberty and union, now and forever, one and inseparable.

Daniel Webster

We hold these truths to be self-evident, that all men are created equal, that they are endowed by their Creator with certain unalienable rights, that among these are life, liberty, and the pursuit of happiness.

The Declaration of Independence

He who looks with pride upon this history which his fathers have written by their heroic deeds, who accepts with gratitude the inheritance which they have bequeathed to him, and who highly resolves to preserve this inheritance unimpaired and to pass it on to his descendants enlarged and enriched, is a true American, be his birthplace or his parentage what it may.

Rev. Lyman Abbott

The four cornerstones of character on which the structure of this nation was built are: Initiative, Imagination, Individuality, and Independence.

Captain Edward V. Rickenbacker

There can be no fifty-fifty Americanism in this country. There is room here for only 100 per cent Americanism, only for those who are Americans and nothing else.

President Franklin D. Roosevelt

Thus too, sail on, O ship of State!
Sail on, O Union, strong and great!
Humanity with all its fears,
With all the hopes of future years,
Is hanging breathless on thy fate!

Henry Wadsworth Longfellow

Grandpa's Farm

Georgia B. Adams

I well remember Grandpa's farm
  Where as a child so small,
I ran to do the barnyard chores
  At Grandpa's beck and call.

He's let me taste the milk so sweet;
  He'd always set aside
A special dish for all the cats;
  Yes, Grandpa really tried

To treat his animals with care;
  He knew them all by name.
Why, I remember one milk cow—
  He used to call her Mayme!

I frolicked in the hayloft and
  I swung upon the swing;
I fed the chickens every day;
  What memories still cling.

He'd take me fishing in the creek;
  We'd hunt for berries, too.
What a delightful time we had
  When I was six-plus-two.

I well remember Grandpa's farm;
  It seems I see it yet.
Nostalgic memories come to mind
  That I just can't forget.

Photo Opposite
FEEDING TIME
Bob Firth
Firth Photobank

The Road to Yesterday

Myrtie Fisher Seaverns

I want to go back to Yesterday,
To the days of long ago;
To wander carefree over the hills
To the haunts I used to know.

I want to search for the Mayflower shy,
Cradled in Earth's warm breast;
To watch the robins as they come North,
To build their cosy nest.

I want to lie on the soft, green grass,
And gaze at the calm, blue sky;
To watch the pictures made by the clouds
As they float lazily by.

I want to drift in an open boat
On the blue, unruffled pond,
Surrounded by misty mountain tops,
And to dream what lies beyond.

I want to roam through the forest dense,
And hark to the fragrant breeze,
As it sings its soothing lullaby
Through the gently swaying trees.

I want to hear the hum of the bees,
To watch the butterflies gay;
I want to stroll through the fields again,
Knee-deep in new-mown hay.

The honeysuckle I want to see,
And smell its sweet perfume;
The gnarled, old lilac beside the door,
With its fragrant, purple bloom.

I want to kneel at my mother's knee,
To say my evening prayer;
To feel once more her loving hand
Upon my tangled hair.

I want to go back to the pirate's cave
Beneath the old hemlock tree;
I want to go back to try to find
The child I used to be.

I want to go back to my rosy dreams
I have lost along the way;
So tell me, please, —I surely must find
The Road to Yesterday.

There's no going back. The road is closed.
The years fly swiftly by.
You can never go back to Yesterday,
No matter how hard you try.

Yesterday's road we may never tread,
The misty past is dead;
But the golden road to Tomorrow
Lies gleaming just ahead.

CRAFTWORKS

Patchwork Table Runner

Marty Sowder Brooks

This delightful, country patchwork table runner will brighten up a 4th of July celebration or any summer picnic. Place the runner directly on the table or over a white tablecloth.

Materials:

- $1/3$ yard 48-inch wide lightweight denim
- 4 $12^1/_2$ inch squares muslin
- $1/4$ yard each of 6 cotton calico fabrics
- $1/8$ yard red bandanna fabric for binding
- Thread to match

Cut calico fabric into bias strips, $3/4$ inches to $2^1/_2$ inches wide. Width should vary to produce a casual and pleasing effect. Lay one of the longer strips, about 16 inches in length, right side up, across the diagonal middle of the muslin square. Pin top and bottom edges.

Place a second strip of a different fabric over the first strip, right sides together with one edge of each strip even. Using a $1/4$-inch seam allowance, stitch along edge of strips, stitching through the muslin. Turn strip right side out and press flat.

Place a strip of a third fabric over the second strip, right sides together with one edge of each strip even. Stitch as before, through 3 layers, with a $1/4$-inch seam allowance.

Continue, choosing fabric in a variety of patterns and saving the longer strips for the center of each square, until the square is covered. Baste around edge; trim calico fabric even with muslin edges. Repeat for additional 3 squares.

Arrange the 4 squares in a pleasing pattern. With right sides together, stitch two of the squares together, using a $1/4$-inch seam allowance. Stitch the remaining squares, forming a runner 48 inches long.

With wrong sides together, pin the denim to the patchwork strip. Baste around all 4 sides. Topstitch the 3 seams that joined the squares; topstitch the edges of some of the diagonal strips, "quilting" the patchwork runner. There is no need to topstitch every strip, but some chosen at random.

Cut 4 $1^1/_2$-inch wide strips of bandanna fabric, 2 strips 13 inches long and 2 strips 49 inches long; piece strips, if necessary. With right sides together, pin edge of strip to long edge of patchwork. Stitch, using a $1/4$-inch seam allowance. Press under $1/4$ inch of strip. Fold bandanna strip over denim and pin in place. Slipstitch or topstitch bandanna. Repeat for all 4 sides. At each corner, fold excess fabric under, concealing raw edges, and slipstitch in place.

If desired, use pinking shears to cut remaining fabric into 16-inch squares for napkins.

Photo Opposite
TABLE RUNNER
Gerald Koser, Photographer

COLLECTOR'S CORNER

D. Fran Morley

Antique Quilts

MARINER'S COMPASS
Photo Courtesy Shelburne Museum
Shelburne, Vermont

Like so many collectible items considered folk-art, quilts were born of necessity. Over the years, simple, patchwork quilts became more elaborate, and quilting grew to include hundreds of intricate and beautiful designs. This growth was surely a reflection of our ancestors' desire to put order and beauty into their lives.

The making of the first quilt is lost in antiquity, but there is no doubt that the first quilt was an attempt to put left-over scraps of fabric to good use. Early quilts were usually "crazy quilts," a jumble of fabric types, sizes, and colors sewn together with little regard for design; but soon women began to put more thought into their quilts. The pattern "Hit and Miss" had fabric pieces trimmed to the same size and shape but not sewn together in any particular order. Another old pattern, "Roman Stripe," called for alternating stripes of dark and light color. From these humble beginnings, our creative ancestors went on to design elaborate patterns of sunbursts, stars, flowers, pine trees, and complex geometric shapes. A sunburst or star design is at first glance a simple and repetitive design, but even the most simple sunburst quilt requires great precision in cutting and sewing and often represents a quilt maker's highest achievement.

It was a matter of pride not to copy another's design, so women entered into quiet competitions to turn out the most beautiful, most elaborate quilt, and quilt designs soon were as varied as the quilters themselves. As quilting progressed, quilts often included renditions of popular symbols, such as the logo for the 1933 Chicago World's Fair or the blue eagle of President Roosevelt's National Recovery Act, making quilts a reflection of society. One of the most popular quilt designs, the "Log Cabin," is a symbol of the American frontier, but westward movement also led to the development of "friendship" quilts—quilts with individual blocks stitched by different women and given as a gift to a departing friend. Friendship quilts were also popular as fund-raisers for churches and social clubs and still are today.

Old and new quilts can often be found at church bazaars, quilt shows, auctions, antique stores, and estate sales. Because of the fragile nature of quilts, really old quilts in fine condition are rare and often very expensive. It is more common to find old quilt fragments made into smaller wall hangings or pillows. Doll quilts or cradle quilts are often found at sales, but truly old versions of these are also rare. Often what is presented as a cradle or doll quilt is actually a cut-down version of a larger quilt. Look for new binding or new stitching at the edge as evidence.

CRAZY QUILT
Photo Courtesy Shelburne Museum
Shelburne, Vermont

A quilt altered in this way may not have the monetary value of a true cradle or doll quilt, but if the color and design are appealing, the quilt is worth purchasing. As with all collectibles, buy what you like. The cost of buying a quilt should be equal to the pleasure derived from owning and displaying it.

However a quilt is displayed, it should be protected from the sun and fabric stress. One method of displaying a quilt is to carefully hand-stitch a suitable fabric around the edge of the old quilt and then wrap this fabric over a frame. Quilts can also be simply draped over a heavy dowel rod, but all displayed quilts need to be taken down periodically for a rest to ease the stress on the old, delicate fabrics. Washing is not recommended for old quilts; however, if a quilt must be cleaned, a professional cleaner accustomed to working with antique fabrics should be consulted. If a quilt is too damaged to be displayed whole, a pretty way to display small quilt fragments is to frame individual squares behind glass and hang them in a wall grouping.

Once a necessity for every home, quilts should be viewed today as the artwork they always have been. From simple patchwork designs to colorful crazy quilts and elaborate geometric designs, quilts offer something for every taste, as well as a glimpse into our past.

71

Country Maids

Bess Truit

When you and I were country maids,
We wore our hair in long, tight braids
Or curled around in ringlets, two,
And tied with ribbons pink and blue.

We never wore stiff frills and lace
Or bright red rouge upon our face.
We never dared to show our knees
No matter, then, how strong the breeze.

Our dresses buttoned down the back.
The skirts were full, there was no lack
Of cloth, to make them high of neck,
Or long of sleeve our arms to deck.

We wore real petticoats you know
To keep us warm and not for show.
When you and I were country maids
And wore our hair in curls and braids.

LITTLE GIRL IN FIELD OF POPPIES
Bear Valley, California
Superstock, Inc.

Country CHRONICLE

Lansing Christman

I t seems that once again people are coming to appreciate items made by hand. Those homemade swings I see suspended from the boughs of a tree in a neighboring country dooryard take me back to my days as a barefoot boy many Junes ago. I don't know who constructed my neighbor's swing, but the swing I remember was made entirely at home. Only the rope came from the general store in the village.

I do not remember the type of wood used, but I know the plank was sawed off neatly at both ends to form a seat that fit snugly into the long loop of rope. The wood was sanded as smooth as silk, and each end of the seat was notched so that no matter how high the swing and rider flew into the sky the swing stayed attached to the rope.

One of my brothers often provided an extra push that sent me soaring out higher and higher;

but what I appreciated most in those young years was to swing slowly and gently, back and forth, on soft summer evenings.

From my gently swinging seat, I had a front-row seat as nature raised the curtain on the evening. I could watch the flickering lights of fireflies as they floated over the dooryard grass and the new-mown hay in the meadow. How sweetly the aroma of the hay drifted into the dooryard. I could listen to the tinkling of cow-bells from a neighbor's pasture on the hill, or the lowing of a cow, or the bleat of a baby lamb calling for its mother. I could hear the croaking of frogs in the swamp and the echoing calls of the cricket orchestra as it tuned up for the coming darkness.

I can still watch fireflies and listen to crickets in my dooryard these years later. But I watch and listen now on a slow evening walk, or from the comforts of my lawn chair as the sun goes down.

As I relax and let the sounds drift over me, I slip back in memory to long-ago summer nights. I remember those evenings of rich content I found as a boy in the bucolic countryside where there were pastures and meadows and climbing hills and homemade wooden swings for soft, gentle swinging.

The author of two published books, Lansing Christman has been contributing to Ideals *for almost twenty years. Mr. Christman has also been published in several American, foreign, and braille anthologies. He lives in rural South Carolina.*

Our Country House

Mildred Jarrell

I recall our country house
Beside a country lane,
And I recall the yesteryears
As I walk the fields again.

The kitchen with its firelight glow,
The table's groaning fare,
The bounty from the fields and trees;
A wealth beyond compare.

The parlor lit with lamplight,
Casting shadows dim,
While sister played the organ,
And we sang an old-time hymn.

The early morning country sounds,
The rooster's crow at dawn,
The lowing of the cattle
As they slowly left the barn.

And I recall when night would fall,
'Twas as quiet as a mouse;
For all were snug in feather beds,
Inside our country house.

COUNTRY LIVING ROOM
Illinois
Jessie Walker Photography

MEMORIES

Garnett Ann Schultz

My heart is filled with memories
Of yesterdays gone by,
With dreams that hold a tender thought
Or sometimes bring a sigh.
I still recall the stream
Where violets smiled at me
And long to feel the summer breeze
Caressing, tenderly.

My thoughts are filled with memories
My heart cannot forget,
The pleasant evenings just at dusk
I shall remember yet:

A walk into a star-filled night,
The moon aglow above,
The quietness of eventide,
Your whispered words of love.

My dreams are dreams of yesterday
Of happiness we've known,
Of little hopes and little joys
We somehow made our own.
A world so full of little things
That mean so much to me,
The beauties Mother Nature lends
That some may never see.

My heart's adrift in memories
The past with gladness rare;
And then from out a clear blue sky
Tomorrow's waiting there
With all that's real and all that's fine
To bring new joys to me;
And then on some far, distant day
Another memory.

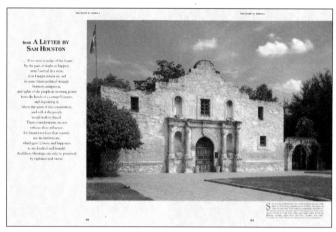